How to
Ride a
Giraffe

by Alice Cary   illustrated by Paul Meisel

GReaT SouRCe
EDUCATION GROUP
A Houghton Mifflin Company

Do you want to ride a giraffe?
Here's what you need:

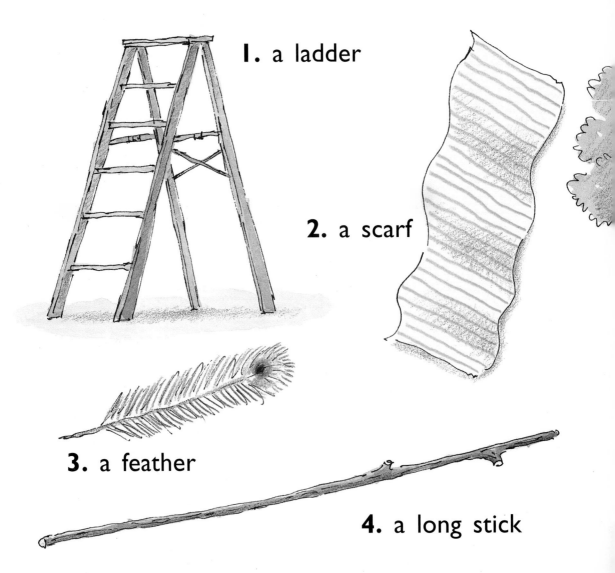

1. a ladder

2. a scarf

3. a feather

4. a long stick

5. a bag of popcorn

popcorn

6. a tree

7. a giraffe!

How to Get on the Giraffe

1. Carry the ladder to the giraffe.

2. Climb the ladder.

3. Put the scarf around the giraffe's neck.

4. Sit down and hold on.

How to Start the Giraffe

1. Say, "Please, let's go."

2. Tickle the giraffe with the feather.

3. Give the giraffe
some popcorn.

4. Hold on.

How to Steer the Giraffe

1. Put some popcorn on the stick.

2. Point the stick left to turn left.

3. Point the stick right to turn right.

WARNING: Do not try to back up.
Backing up could be dangerous.

How to Have a Safe Trip

1. Don't get caught in a dog leash.

2. Don't walk under clotheslines.

3. Don't walk near telephone wires.

4. Don't ride on merry-go-rounds.

How to Get Off the Giraffe

1. Find a tree.

2. Grab the tree
and hold on.

3. Call for the ladder.

Things to Remember

1. Feed the giraffe every day.
(He likes popcorn.)

2. Keep the giraffe clean.

3. Find a good parking space for the giraffe.

4. Always put money in the parking meter.